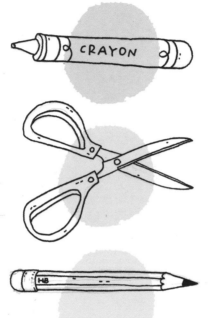

Published by Collins
An imprint of HarperCollins Publishers
Westerhill Road, Bishopbriggs,
Glasgow G64 2QT

www.harpercollins.co.uk

© HarperCollins Publishers 2018

Collins® is a registered trademark
of HarperCollins Publishers Ltd.

Illustrations © Clare Forrest
Text © Penny Alexander and Becky Goddard-Hill

978-0-00-830121-7

Printed in Great Britain by Bell and Bain Ltd

10 9 8 7 6 5 4 3

Thanks to Laura Waddell, Keith Moore
and all the team at HarperCollins
for championing happiness. Thank you
Clare Forrest for the magical illustrations.

Becky - Thanks to lovely GG who
always encouraged me and taught me
that you can always find joy if you keep
your heart open and your smile bright.
And to my children, Frankie and Annalise,
who absolutely make the world a happier
place to be.

Penny - Thanks to my parents Angela
and Alan for the happiness tools, Rik for
refusing to be anything but happy and Lily
and Gylan for all the happiness you bring.

Thanks to all who bravely choose
to Create Your Own Happy, may
your happy actions spread far and wide.

#CYOHappy

colour me!

cReAte YouR OWN HAPPY

Penny Alexander
and
Becky Goddard-Hill

illustrated by Clare Forrest

Introduction

Your happiness is a superpower.

Do you know how powerful you are?

You are so powerful you can create your own happy life every single day.

No matter what is going on (annoying sibling/late homework/missed TV show) there are always ways you can make your day better and brighter. This book is full of fun activities that will show you how.

Is happiness the most important thing in life?

Well that's a very BIG question and it all depends on what you believe BUT we believe that almost everyone would be in agreement that being happy is important and pretty fantastic. Whereas being unhappy? Well, that's just a bit pants, isn't it?

About this book

The activities in this book will help you learn
to be happier no matter what is going on in your life.
They will teach you to be resilient and positive and
optimistic and they will teach you to be kind to yourself
and to look after your physical and emotional health.

PART ONE is about making yourself happy,
PART TWO is about making others happy, which also
has the power to make YOU happier at the same time,
and PART THREE is about making a happier world,
another way to boost your own happy levels.

None of it is complicated, all of it is fun and in every
scenario YOU make the happy happen.

The big thing about this book is the WHY?
For every activity we've explained the science
behind it, WHY it works. Because let's face it, who
wants to do anything unless they know WHY it works?

How to use this book

It is totally up to you how you use this book, you can do it by yourself, with a friend or with an adult. You could even take it in to school and suggest you do one of the activities as a lesson.

You can do it in order, you can do it backwards or even start in the middle.

You can share your answers with other people or you can keep it really private. Stick things in if you want, or cut things out of it. You are in charge. This is all about YOU creating your happiness – so over to you now. We do hope you have fun and learn some cool stuff along the way.

So, are you up for the challenge ... are you ready to be the creator of your own happiness?

making
YOURSELF
HAPPY

You've got this

Sometimes life is just great, isn't it? You are star of the week, your birthday is coming up, you had the best ice cream for tea and have a sleepover planned. How easy it is to be happy when life is good.

Other times you have days of tests or feel poorly and your friends are leaving you out. Sad times.

But you know, these things don't have to get you down.

You can still make your days happy and things better even when life is hard because we are going to show you that it's always possible to make yourself happy. It doesn't just depend on other people, luck or what's going on around you.

You are in control of a large part of your happiness. You are strong and smart and have bouncebackability (that's the ability to bounce back when life is tough).

Happiness starts with you

If you are on an aeroplane, safety advisors will tell you to put on your own oxygen mask first before you help anyone else with theirs. This applies to happiness too. If you are happy first, it is so much easier to help other people be happy. So working on your own happiness is essential if you want to be a force of happiness in the world.

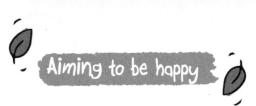
Aiming to be happy

John Lennon was a musician in a very famous band called The Beatles. He was also very wise. Here's what he had to say about happiness...

When I was 5 years old, my mother always told me that happiness was the key to life. When I went to school, they asked me what I wanted to be when I grew up. I wrote down 'happy'. They told me I didn't understand the assignment, and I told them they didn't understand life.

Wanting to be happy is a great aim for when you are an adult, but it is also a wonderful aim to have RIGHT NOW ... EVERY. SINGLE. DAY.

So next time an adult asks you what you want to be when you grow up you can tell them the same – you want to be happy!
It might just make them think.

WhEn I gRoW uP I WANT To BE hAPpy ✓

This section of the book is full of activities to help you take control of your own happiness. Making yourself happy is powerful and fun.

1. What really makes you happy?

Be thankful for what you have; you'll end up having more. If you concentrate on what you don't have, you will never, ever have enough.
 – Oprah Winfrey (Actress and TV show host)

DID YOU KNOW THAT HAPPINESS IS MADE UP OF:

50% genes and upbringing
10% circumstances beyond you, like money or life events

But here is the cool bit ... happiness is
40% things you can control yourself, like your attitude, relationships, hobbies and activities.

That's a whole lot of happiness YOU can shape yourself. This book is full of ideas to help you do just that, but let's get an idea first of who you are and what makes you happiest.

Activity: Happy collage

Think about all the things that make you happy. This can be a tricky task, and only you know the truth!

Close your eyes. Take some time to remember the things that have brought a smile to your face and filled you with energy and excitement during the last week.

Remember to look for:

- BIG and SMALL things
- Things that don't cost anything — colours, smells, weather, sounds, words
- Things you do — games, activities, hobbies, special moments
- People — friends, family, inspiring people
- Pets and animals
- Things you LOVE!

Create a collage of the things that make you happy. You could write them in coloured letters or draw them or do a mix of both. You could even cut out pictures or stick in photos if you want to. Use colour and fill the space! You could put a timer on for 3 minutes if you are worried you won't be able to think of anything. Timers are great for making our brains go faster!

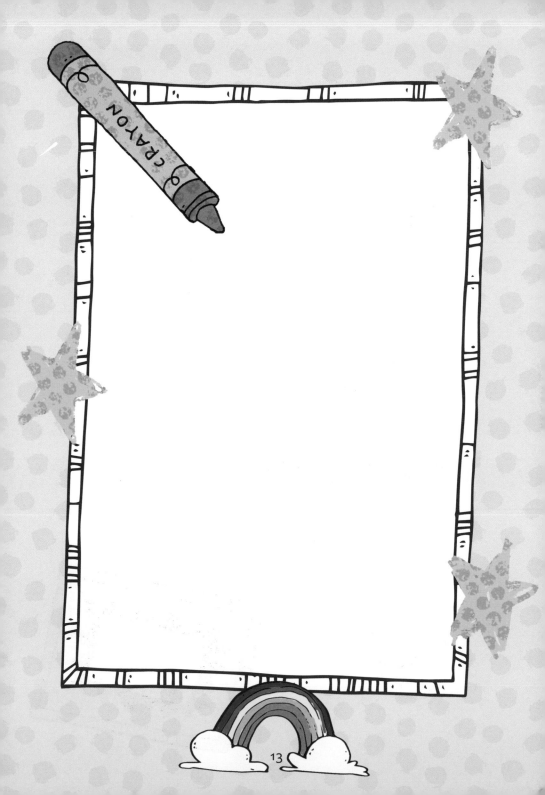

So how did it go?

Looking at your collage, is there anything you had forgotten about that makes you happy? Does anything about it surprise you? When did you last do something that makes you happy?

How it works

Images are a powerful way of making things stick in our minds. Research has shown that creating a display of something you want (a 'vision board'), helps to bring it to life. When athletes create a vision in their heads of crossing the finish line or holding a medal, they succeed more often! What we give our focus to can start to grow. Knowing what makes us happy helps us to DESIGN our own happy life.

Create your own happy...

...by looking back at the collage whenever you need to find something to cheer you up. Don't forget to add new happy things as you find them in this book!

my happy life

2. What are your signature strengths?

Comparison is the thief of joy.
– Theodore Roosevelt, 26th President
of the United States of America.

Have you ever compared yourself to someone else and felt your happiness levels falling? Perhaps because they are taller, or seem funnier, more popular or better at something?

Comparing ourselves to others really can steal our happiness. Instead, flip this and build a list of what makes you UNIQUE. Knowing yourself and celebrating yourself builds your self-esteem. Self-esteem is your confidence in your OWN worth and what YOU are able to achieve.

Activity: Handful of strengths

Start by thinking about what makes YOU unique. What are your signature strengths – the things that set you apart from others? Think about hobbies, school and things you do for other people. Don't forget that things such as helping others, smiling and being kind are JUST as important.

On the next page draw round one of your hands.

SUPERPOWER

draw your
hand here

a helping hand

ring finger
middle finger
index finger
pinky
thumb

Once you have completed the outline write one
of your strengths in each finger or thumb.

Here are some prompts to help you:

- Something that my friends like about me is...
- I'm proud of...
- My family was happy when I...
- I'm good at...

Stuck? Ask friends and family, they are bound to think of something you have forgotten. Don't forget to tell them what you like about them too – showing gratitude makes you happier and hearing compliments makes others happier!

So how did it go?

What are you uniquely good at? These are your signature strengths. Could you do them more often? When?

How it works

Researchers found that people who exercised their signature strengths every day became significantly happier for months at a time!

Create your own happy...

...by looking back at your hand diagram when you need a happiness boost and a reminder of what makes you YOU! Make a plan to practice your signature strengths at a specific time or event each day. After you accomplish it, reward yourself.

creative

HAPPY

3. Express yourself

Feelings are just visitors, let them come and go
— Mooji (Spiritual teacher)

Feelings kept hidden inside can jumble up your thoughts. Writing them down or talking about them can make you feel both happier and healthier. It just takes practice.

Activity: Getting your feelings out

Write down three feelings (positive or negative) which you have had today and what caused them.

SAD

happy

1. Today I felt ....
   because ....

inspired

2. Today I felt ....
   because ....

3. Today I felt ....
   because ....

happy

So how did it go?

Did it feel good to get your feelings out? Did you find it easier to talk about your positive feelings than your negative ones?

How it works

Scientists have found that keeping all our bad feelings inside can actually make us feel unwell! Letting our feelings out by talking about them or writing them down is a way of keeping ourselves healthy, like getting enough exercise, cleaning our teeth or eating our five a day.

So does it make you a weak person if you say you feel sad? No way! It makes you a stronger, healthier and happier person.

Create your own happy...

...by talking or writing about how you feel. Expressing some feelings might take practice. It is easy to say, 'Chocolate makes me happy!' but harder to say, 'I feel really jealous because my friend got in the football team and I didn't.' Negative feelings get smaller when you talk about them with someone you trust. But, if you let out your happy feelings these get BIGGER. So make sure you share your happy feelings too.

4. Get moving, get happy!

Motivation is what gets you started. Habit is what keeps you going.

- Jim Ryun (Former athlete and politician)

Experts say young people should do at least 60 minutes of exercise a day, but why?

Obviously we know exercise keeps your body fit and healthy, but did you know it also makes you happier?

People who move regularly are happier than those who don't. Scientists at Cambridge University tracked people using an app on their phones and found people who had been moving felt happier than those who had been sitting still.

The trick to keeping up exercise is making it a habit. Plan it into your day just like cleaning your teeth, going to school or eating tea.

Activity: Move it!

Write down the exercise you already do each day of the week and how long you do it for. It might be PE lessons, dancing, sports clubs, or walking to and from school.

Next let's fill in the gaps, you need to be active for at least an hour a day.

You might need to try a few things before you find an activity you love. Not everyone likes team sports, but swimming, walking, climbing, jogging or cycling can be great if you prefer to exercise without competing against others.

Dance or yoga classes are brilliant ways to boost happy feelings, and Cubs, Brownies, Scouts and Guides all involve games that get you moving.

Next let's think of some 10-minute mood-boosting exercises you can do whenever you have been sitting still for too long watching TV, in the car or doing homework. You could:

- Dance to three of your favourite songs
- Find a YouTube exercise video for young people —yoga, stretching, learning a dance routine
- Try an exercise from the ChangetLife website
- Create an assault course around the house, this could be great fun with brothers, sisters, parents or friends — jump from cushion to cushion, climb under chairs or tables, balance a piece of fruit on a spoon, hop, wheelbarrow.
- Walk the dog if you have one, or someone else's

Can you add some mood boosters to each day?

22

So how did it go?

Were you doing enough exercise? Did you fill your week? Which 10-minute challenges did you like best?

How it works

Happiness isn't just in our head, it's actually made all over our bodies. Scientists have proved that exercise improves our mood and decreases feelings of depression, anxiety and stress. When we move our bodies make endorphins, chemicals which help produce positive feelings. Bodies are basically happiness-making factories.

Create your own happy by...

...exercising with friends and family, which can really help to make it more fun and easier to stick to. Once you have found a sport you enjoy, you could set a goal, join a competition or a team, set a distance to run, swim or cycle together, choose a tricky skill to perfect, or simply exercise for five weeks in a row.

5. Create Your Own Happy Jar

Enjoy the little things, for one day you may look back and realize they were the big things.

— Robert Brault (Writer)

Sometimes our minds play tricks on us. Have you ever noticed that when one thing goes wrong we tend to get stuck on that? All the brilliant little things that have happened seem to vanish and all we can think about is the one bad thing.

This is where the 'Create Your Own Happy' Jar comes in very handy. Happiness experts have discovered that two of the biggest secrets to happiness are actually VERY simple:

1. Notice the little things that make you happy
2. Express gratitude

Activity: Make a happy jar

It is so easy to make a 'Create Your Own Happy' Jar – a place to keep a record of all the little amazing things that happen.

YOU WILL NEED:
- A jam jar with a lid
- Colouring pens or permanent markers
- Plain paper or sticky labels
- Glue or sellotape
- Stickers (optional)
- Small pieces of paper
- A pen

Soak the jam jar in hot soapy water to remove the label and let it dry out.

In the meantime colour or design your own label. This could be on a piece of paper you stick onto the jar, a plain sticky label or if you have permanent markers, you could draw straight onto the glass.

If you have stickers you could decorate your jar with them too. Your jar needs to be something that totally grabs your attention and feels full of happy.

Next, take some small pieces of paper and think of the awesome things that have happened to you in the last week. Remember they don't have to be big things. Here are some ideas to get you started:

- Getting a smile from someone special
- Hearing a favourite song play on the radio
- Receiving praise from a teacher
- Seeing a rainbow
- Inventing a new game
- Laughing at a funny joke
- Learning something new
- Experiencing a lovely smell
- Reaching a new level in a game
- Enjoying some good weather

Even on a really bad day, remember tomorrow is a new day, and you can always write: 'I survived a really tough day today.'

Make sure your jar is somewhere where you will see it every day – maybe by your bed so you can record the happy moments before you sleep?

colour me!

CREATE
YOUR
OWN
HAPPY

So how did it go?

Look back at your jar after a week, a month. Are you surprised by the things you had forgotten about? How does it feel to remember the awesome stuff?

How it works

Sometimes we become so fixed on the big things in life that we forget to celebrate the little moments of happy. As the quote reminds us above, sometimes the little things are just as important as the big things. If we remember to notice and be grateful for all the little moments of happy, it gives us a huge mood boost, which helps us feel more positive when things don't go to plan. Sometimes we have to train our brains to focus on the happy!

Create your own happy...

...by looking in your jar from time to time and remembering all the brilliant things you have done. You could make a note to remind yourself in a diary or calendar.

6. Let it go

Outer order contributes to inner calm
— Gretchen Rubin (Happiness expert)

We all have so much stuff and lots of it just lies around not being used at all (this applies to adults too!). The things you have outgrown are just taking up space in your room. It's time to pass them on.

Decluttering and passing on your unwanted stuff may sound like chores but in fact they will make you happy. Firstly, having less clutter around gives you much more space and makes things you do want to use or play with much easier to find. Secondly, when you give things to other people you feel good too.

Activity: Sort and share

Find 3 things you can pass on to someone you know and 3 things you can give to a charity shop. Pop them in a box and put them by your front door to remind you to pass them on just as soon as you can.

Which 6 things did you choose? Draw in the boxes overleaf all the items you have decided to give away.

So how did it go?

How did it feel to declutter? Has it made you want to give more things away? Does your room look better without so much stuff in it?

How it works

Our brains are calmer when we live in a calm and tidy place. Clutter and mess cause us to have higher cortisol levels in our brain by overwhelming our senses, and this makes us stressed.
This stress makes it hard for us to get things done (like homework!).

Brain scientists have found we are more productive, less irritable and less distracted in a clutter-free environment.

Create your own happy...

...by passing on the games you no longer play, the clothes you no longer fit or the books you no longer read.

If you can't think of someone to pass things on to, why not donate your stuff to a charity shop or take it to a recycling centre? You will feel good about helping a charity and your parents will be pretty happy that you are having a clear out too!

It can feel really freeing to let go of things that are no longer of use to us. This can apply to lots of things actually, not just our belongings. If we let go of friendships that don't work any more, hobbies we are no longer interested in and arguments that are going nowhere we will often feel relieved and we will have more space for new or better things in our lives. We don't need to hold tightly to things that don't make us happy, letting go can create a lot of happiness.

FREE TO A GOOD HOME!

7. Become a Confident Speaker

If you're not comfortable with public speaking – and nobody starts out comfortable; you have to learn how to be comfortable – practice. I cannot overstate the importance of practicing. – Hillary Clinton (Politician)

Breathe in confidence. Breathe out doubt.

Speaking to people can sometimes feel scary, so here are some tricks to make you feel more confident about sharing your thoughts out loud.

Activity: Speak up!

Set a timer for one minute, choose a topic or ask someone to make one up for you. Can you keep talking about it for one minute? Here are some things you could talk about:

- My awesome hobbies
- My family and pets
- My favourite YouTube or TV show
- My friends

Remember, we can all feel nervous about talking in front of others; even YouTubers and politicians have to practice.

Here are some tips to help you:

- Practise speaking out loud in front of a mirror
- Stand up straight, put your shoulders back, put your head up and smile! Body language tells people you are confident, even if you don't feel it inside. It also tells your brain you are confident.
- If you feel nervous take a deep breath or two. Breathe in through your nose and count to five. Then breathe out through your mouth as you count to five again.

So how did it go?

Which topics can you talk about most confidently?

How it works

Have you ever felt a bit shaky, jumpy or tense when you have to speak in front of people? This is because of a substance that our bodies make when we feel nervous. It is called adrenaline. Our bodies make it naturally when we are stressed and also when we feel angry or excited.

Adrenaline helps us by making our hearts beat faster to give us more energy for a performance. By thinking of these funny, nervous feelings as useful things you can feel differently about them. Actors and sports people think of nerves in this way, which is how they stay confident.

Create your own happy...

...by building your confidence. Put yourself forward to be a class rep, sport team leader or part of the class council. Practise speaking up, because the more you do it the more normal it feels and the better you get at it. Speaking confidently means you share all your ideas with the world, which can help your dreams come true. Speaking out to help others can help make them happier too.

8. Create a laughter kit

A good laugh is sunshine in the house
— William Thackery (Novelist)

Laughing always makes us feel lighter, brighter and happier. But, how can we make ourselves laugh when nothing seems funny?

Activity: Make a laughter kit

Your laughter kit can be in a box or a bag or on a shelf in a cupboard. It doesn't matter where you create it, it is what you put in it that counts. Every single item should be designed to make you giggle. Everyone has different things that make them laugh but some ideas you might include in your laughter kit are:

- A joke book
- Some nonsense poetry
- A DVD that has you in stitches
- Some daft pranks (like fake poo)
- A hilarious book
- A journal where you have written down funny stories or perhaps a funny game.

Give yourself an hour to gather together your laughter kit.

Draw or write what you have put in your kit below.

So how did it go?

Was putting your laughter kit together fun? When might you use it? Was it easy to think of lots of things that make you laugh or was it a struggle? If it was hard then it was most definitely worth it. You clearly need a lot more FUNNY in your life!

How it works

Laughter has some brilliant benefits. It affects a bit of our brain which releases the feel-good hormones called endorphins. These chemicals make us feel happy. Laughing can also help our muscles relax for up to 45 minutes afterwards which soothes away any tension or stress in our bodies. Laughter is the best medicine!

One study found that children laugh as much as 400 times per day compared to grumpy adults who only laugh fifteen times a day – you might well need to share that laughter kit with your grown-ups, it sounds like they probably need it more than you do!

Create your own happy..

...by adding to your laughter kit all the time so it's constantly fresh and funny. Maybe you could ask your friends for funny DVD suggestions, get a new joke book for your birthday or spend your pocket money on some pranks?

9. Stay creative, stay happy

The best way to get something done is to begin.

– Author unknown

Creativity isn't just about glue and paint. Experts say that creativity is the ability to come up with new ideas, make new links between ideas and to come up with new solutions to problems. You could be an artist, an engineer, a designer, a poet, a mathematician, or a scientist and still use creativity.

Happiness experts know that getting into 'the flow' of creative activity makes us happier, but this can be tricky sometimes!

When we were little we didn't worry about getting things wrong, but as we grow up trying to be perfect and planning the final outcome can smother our creativity. Worrying about making mistakes can stop us getting started in the first place.

Putting things off is called procrastinating, and it's a habit that can really drain our happiness. Being creative is about letting our minds play freely.

Activity: Find 'the flow'!

Choose one of these four creativity-unlocking activities, you never know where it might take you!

1. Write a short story in the space below. Don't stop, just write whatever comes into your head and focus on getting to the end of the page. Don't cross out or change anything. If you can't think of anything to write try the starting point: 'I opened the box...'

colour me!

2. Invent a tool that could solve all your problems. Draw it here.

3. Choose a page in a book. Using the first, fifth, thirteenth and last word on that page, write a poem. You have 5 minutes!

4. Draw yourself, or a friend or pet or object, four times over. The first time take 10 seconds, second 30 seconds, the third one minute, the fourth five minutes.

So how did it go?

Did the activities help you create anything you didn't expect? Is it good to just go for it without worrying about the outcome sometimes?
Did you find 'the flow'?

How it works

When we are in what psychologists call 'the flow' with a task, we feel happy. When we are happy we come up with creative solutions more easily. We just need to allow ourselves to get started!

The famous American novelist EL Doctorow said that creative writing was like *'driving in the dark'*. In other words, you can't see the final destination (the end of the story), but you might find it if you can just keep following the headlights (writing) rather than stopping the car (your brain) to think too much!

Create your own happy...

...by enjoying creative play without worrying about the outcome! You never know where your amazingly creative brain might take you. Remember you don't have to be perfect at something to enjoy it.

10. Learn to Relax

Tension is who you think you should be,
relaxation is who you are.   – Chinese proverb.

We can be our happiest and most real selves when we are feeling truly relaxed. And when our brains relax, amazing things can happen! Lots of people say they get their best ideas when relaxing – in the shower, in bed, riding in a car. JK Rowling thought of her Harry Potter stories when she was staring out of a train window. The 11-year-old violinist, Alama Deutscher writes stage musicals and says she has her best ideas when she is skipping. English Scientist Issac Newton was sitting under an apple tree, chilling out, when an apple fell right in front of his eyes and he came up with his world famous explanation of gravity.

Activity: Relaxation exercise

Learn to relax completely in only 30 seconds!

Find a quiet place where you won't be interrupted, and turn off the TV and music.

Take a full breath and then count to 30 following the instructions below. Counting a little more each time makes you take slightly longer breaths and these longer breaths work to calm you down. If this doesn't make you feel totally relaxed the first time, try another 30 seconds. Repeat until you feel super calm.

BREATHE IN, count 1
— Breathe out count 2

BREATHE IN, count 3,4
— Breathe out count 5,6

BREATHE IN, count 7,8,9
— Breathe out count 10,11,12

BREATHE IN, count 13,14,15,16
— Breathe out count 17,18,19,20

BREATHE IN, count 21,22,23,24,25
— Breathe out count 26,27,28,29,30

Tip - use your fingers to tap out the rising number of counts in each breath so you don't lose track.

So how did it go?

Do you feel more relaxed and calm? What helps you to relax? Where do you feel relaxed?

In the space below, draw your favourite place to relax or something you could think about to help you relax.

How it works

Scientists have found that regular relaxation is like an awesome ninja. It fights off stress and anxiety and leaves us happier. When we switch off, our relaxation ninjas are hard at work breaking up worries, relieving aches and pains, supercharging our immune system and making sure our heart is pumping at exactly the right beats per minute. Sometimes the things we think calm us, like TV, are not that relaxing. Television's gentle flickering lowers our brainwaves and distracts us. This can be good if we need to stop thinking about the day, but it doesn't let our mind empty or our body completely rest.

Regular relaxation is just as important as eating healthy food or getting enough sleep and exercise.

Create your own happy...

...by relaxing for at least 10 minutes every day. You could do this staring out of the window, in a chair or in a car or bus. You could lie on the grass and look up into trees or make shapes out of the clouds. You could make a relaxation den in your bedroom, with cushions and pictures or photos of somewhere where you feel truly relaxed to inspire you.

11. Use Music to change your mood

I often think in music. I live my daydreams in music. I see my life in terms of music.
                    – Albert Einstein, Theoretical Physicist

Scientists have proved that upbeat music can make us feel happier, but you don't need to be Einstein to work that out – just listen to some happy music and see what happens.

Activity: Make a happiness mix

Make a list of your favourite songs. You can choose songs that remind you of happy times, or songs that make you smiley, excited or full of energy. You could also ask your family or friends to suggest some happy songs.

Now use your list of favourite songs to create your own happy playlist. There are lots of ways to do this on and offline, so you might need to ask an adult to help you with this.

Listen to your playlist every day for 10 days. Before you listen, score your mood out of 10, using 10 for super happy and 0 for really not. Then score your mood again after you have listened and see if it has made a difference.

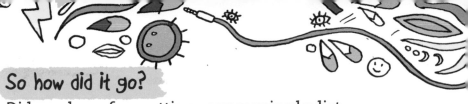

So how did it go?

Did you have fun putting your music playlist together? Did music make a difference to how you felt? Did music help you out of an unhappy mood?

How it works

As we listen, music gets to work on our nervous system, sending messages from our brain to our body. These messages control our blood pressure and heartbeat. Music also sends messages to our brain that can change our feelings and emotions. Research with 1,000 pupils who took singing classes found they were happier at school. Music really can affect our bodies and minds. Amazing!

Create your own happy...

...by making themed music mixes. You could make a music mix to make you feel energetic and another to make you feel relaxed. Use your music to change your mood, or even to cheer up a friend.

My hAPPy Music List

1. _____
2. _____
3. _____
4. _____
5. _____
6. _____
7. _____
8. _____
9. _____
10. _____

12. Become a worry ninja

Drag your thoughts away from your troubles... by the ears, by the heels, or any other way you can manage it.　　　　　　　　　— Mark Twain (Author)

The more we focus on our worries the bigger they become, so it is really useful to know how to stop ourselves worrying quite so much.

We do not want to overfocus on our worries but we do need to be able to express them, get help and support with them or let them go. In fact what we need to do is CONTROL our worries so our worries don't take over and control us, so let's practice!

Activity: Plan a Worry Session

You need a two-step plan of attack.

Step One:

Decide when, where and with whom you want to think about your worries. A 20-minute slot once a day is definitely enough. Making a set time to deal with them rather than constantly going over and over them in your mind will really help.

Write a plan for your Worry Session here.

Where ....
When ....
Who with..........................

Step Two:
When it's time for your Worry Session, sit with someone you trust (or just by yourself) and try to answer these worry-busting questions:

- What is my worry? (Name it)
- Is it likely to happen? (Check the facts)
- What can I do about this worry to make it better? When and how will I do this? (Make a plan)
- If I can't do anything to lessen this worry, what might help to distract me from it? (Accept it for now and give your brain a break)

Distractions may include watching a movie, reading a great book, dancing, baking, etc. Can you think of some other things you could do...?

By choosing a time and place to think about your worries and ways to overcome them, you will be IN CONTROL of them and that will feel so much better.

So how did it go?

Did you find it easy to save your worries for your Worry Session? If you struggle with this, try just writing them down as they come into your head but don't think about them any more until it's time to. You are in control!

Did the questions in Step Two help you come up with any solutions?

How it works

According to scientists our brains are designed to worry first and think second because the emotional part of our brain is quicker to react than the thinking part of our brain. This is often why we can worry unnecessarily and our emotions can feel in charge. Taking a step-by-step THINKING approach to worries can take the emotion out of them and help you feel more in control. We can all learn to think first if we keep practicing.

Create your own happy...

...by being the one who decides when to worry and what to do about your worries. You are in charge of your worries – you are a worry-busting ninja.

13. Plan your happy day

Most of us are just about as happy as we make up our minds to be. — William Adams (Adventurer)

Even if the day ahead seems gloomy (maybe you have a test or feel poorly?) you can still plan it to include some bright and happy things to look forward to. It may not sound fun but being organised will definitely make you happy. You are the designer, the painter and the sculptor of your own life to a large extent and it is super helpful to know this.

Activity: Plan your happy

Each morning for the next week, right after breakfast, try sitting down and filling in your happiness goals for the day. Write in three things every day that you KNOW will make you happy and commit to doing them. Ideas could include phoning your best friend, playing your happy music, taking your dog for a long walk or watching your favourite TV show.

think first

On the next page, fill in the planner then tick off the activities as you do them.

HAPPINESS PLANNER

	1	2	3
M Monday			
T Tuesday			
W Wednesday			
T Thursday			
F Friday			
S Saturday			
S Sunday			

So how did it go?

Did you find it easy to think up three happiness activities each day? Did you always get them done? How nice did it feel to decide on your own happiness?

How it works

After lots of research, happiness expert Paul Dolan has come up with a brilliant happiness formula. He has found out that *'happy people pay attention to the everyday experiences that give them pleasure and purpose, then organize their lives so that they are doing more of those things'.* So there you go – simples! You just plan a day with lots of stuff in it that you know will make you happy and it will totally balance out any unhappy stuff you have to deal with!

Create your own happy...

...starting every day with a happiness plan. Try to have a good balance of activities. Some might be social, some sporty, and some relaxing. Also plan WHEN you are you going to do them. Having definite time slots and a thought-out plan will make sure you get things done.

You have the power to make every day have some HAPPY in it!

14. Being Mindful

Mindfulness is a state of active, open attention on the present. – Psychology Today magazine.

Being mindful is about being absolutely in the moment – being aware of your thoughts, feelings, body sensations and the world around you. It is about observing what is happening now. It can be really helpful to focus on right now and calming your mind down, especially if you have been busy thinking about things that have gone wrong in the past or worrying about the future.

Activity: Create a calm down jar

YOU WILL NEED:

- A jam jar with a lid
- Hot water
- 3 tbsp of glitter glue
- Hand soap
- A few drops of food colouring
- 2 tsp of fine glitter

RECIPE:

- Add warm water to your jar until it reaches around a third of the way up
- Add the glitter glue and stir it into the water
- Add a tiny drop of hand soap
- Add a few drops of food colour and give it a good whisk around — the more drops the more intense the colour will be
- Pour in the glitter and stir really well
- Fill your jar with the rest of the warm water, leaving a little gap at the top
- You can glue on the lid or otherwise screw it super tight

This jar is a good way to help you really focus yourself on the present, which in turn helps to calm your mind down if you feel antsy. Simply make sure everything is quiet and that you won't be disturbed, sit really comfortably and shake the jar. Then just watch as the floating glitter settles to the bottom. Let your thoughts and feelings come and go and breathe deeply and slowly. Try to be really aware of what you are looking at and keep focused on the jar.

Repeat it if you don't feel calm, and keep going until you do.

You could make a few of these in different colours and even make some up as gifts for friends.

So how did it go?

Did this calm your mind and make you feel more relaxed? Was it hard not to get distracted?

How it works

Science tells us the amygdala (a part of our brain) has a natural fight, flight, or freeze response when we feel worried or anxious. This makes it hard for us to make good decisions and be in control of our emotions. Mindfulness practice has been shown to make this bit of our brain smaller. The smaller the amygdala becomes, the less stressed people feel, even if nothing else changes.

Create your own happy...

...by trying lots of different mindfulness activities. Here are some ideas:

- Sitting in the garden listening for lots of different sounds
- Taking a walk and noting how many different trees you see
- Eating really slowly and really tasting your food
- Drawing waves on a page and taking a deep breath in and out as you draw a wave going up or down
- Stroking a cat and noticing exactly how your hands feel on their soft fur

15. How to be more positive

If you tell yourself you feel fine, you will.
— Jodi Picoult (Author)

If you think you are weak, fearful, anxious or stupid it will make you feel and often act that way, because what we think about most of the time just gets bigger and bigger. So you need to plant other ideas in your head instead, and focus on the GOOD stuff like how strong, capable, smart and FABULOUS you are.

Activity: Train your brain

Have a go at these 2 positivity activities:

1. Look at yourself in the mirror and name ten fab things about you — say them LOUD and PROUD. Do this every day until you totally believe what you are saying!
(Ask your family or friends if you can't think of ten things, I bet they can!)

2. Do this wordsearch, circling every single positive word that applies to you...
(there will be lots).

```
f u n n y a n t s r c o
u v i n e v i t i s o p
g w c x v b t n e q n t
e e e m a m s i x p f i
z u n c r w e j c a i m
y d q t b t n k i l d i
k e x i l j n l t l e s
z i v a n e h e i m n t
y w n f b u p e n n t i
g h u d a r i n g t o c
l o y a l j g n i r a c
I m a g i n a t i v e x
```

funny	optimistic	brave
nice	positive	confident
daring	imaginative	gentle
exciting	unique	caring
kind	honest	loyal

So how did it go?

Which of these activities worked best for you? Did focusing on the positive stuff in your life make the negative stuff seem smaller?

How it works

Whatever we feed our brain tends to happen. If we think we want to eat a biscuit our brain sends a message to our arm to pick up the biscuit and put it in our mouth where we will chew it. We take this for granted. It is really helpful. On a less helpful note if we think about something that frightens us we can end up shivering and quivering as if that thought was a reality.

It makes sense then that what we think about we tend to create. This can be a problem if we think about things that make us sad or anxious for the majority of our time. Scientists tell us we can actually train our brains to be more positive by making ourselves think positively when we are sad. This brain training is called neuroplasticity and it will actually change how our brains work till positive thinking becomes a habit.

When we have a 'fixed mindset' we just accept things as they turn out and believe we cannot change in any meaningful way, and this can make us feel like failures. This is not helpful. When we are positive we have something called a 'growth mindset' which means when things go 'wrong' we see it as a challenge and something we can learn from rather than as failure. This really helps us try again and keep our spirits up!

Create your own happy...

...by making sure you think about positive stuff at least FOUR times as much as you think about negative stuff. So if you catch yourself something saying negative or grumpy, stop and say something positive and happy instead.

16. Being Brave

You miss 100% of the shots you don't take
    – Wayne Gretzky (Ice hockey player)

Often we call brave people 'fearless'. But courage isn't fearlessness. As Nelson Mandela (South Africa's first black president) said: '*...the brave man is not he who does not feel afraid, but he who conquers that fear.*' (Obviously this applies to women, girls, boys and animals too!)

Life is full of exciting and wonderful opportunities but if you are too scared to get involved you miss out. Being brave can lead to magical adventures and lots of fun.

Bravery is like everything else: the more you practice it, the easier it becomes.

Activity: Courage goals

What do you wish you were brave enough to do? Think of:

- A brave little thing ....
- A brave medium-sized thing ....
- A brave big thing ....

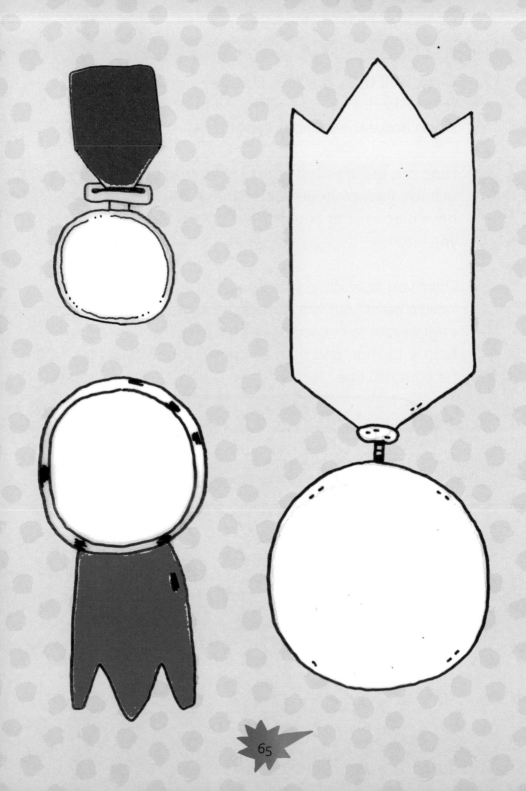

Okay, well these are your Courage Goals. Let's go for it! Like anything at all……the more you practice being brave the easier it becomes.

Here is a list of Fear Busters that could help you achieve your courage goal: choose one and then have a go at your brave little thing. Which one will you choose?

Once you have done your brave little thing then have a go at your brave medium-sized thing. You might want to choose a few more fear busters to help with that, and then some more when you go for your BIG one.

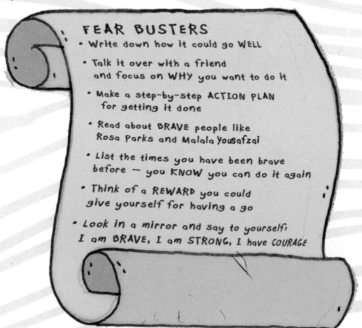

FEAR BUSTERS
- Write down how it could go WELL
- Talk it over with a friend and focus on WHY you want to do it
- Make a step-by-step ACTION PLAN for getting it done
- Read about BRAVE people like Rosa Parks and Malala Yousafzai
- List the times you have been brave before — you KNOW you can do it again
- Think of a REWARD you could give yourself for having a go
- Look in a mirror and say to yourself: I am BRAVE, I am STRONG, I have COURAGE

Keep practising and using your fear busters till being brave is just part of who you are!

So how did it go?

Please, please do tell us how this went! We are so excited to hear about your bravery. And do tell someone else about your being brave and how you did it – you might just inspire them too. Did it make you happy to be brave?

How it works

Neuroscience (brain studies) tells us that courage is not something we are just born with but actually something we can build and make stronger through lots of practice. So, just like learning complicated maths we just have to keep on doing it till it's easy! Once we begin seeing ourselves as brave people we become much more likely to act that way too.

Create your own happy...

...keeping on giving yourself bravery challenges like saying HI! to the new kid, trying a new food, making a phone call when you are nervous or telling your teacher you need extra help. The more you practice the less scary it will be.

17. Happy Healthy You

Our bodies are our gardens, to which our wills are gardeners. – William Shakespeare (Playwright)

Shakespeare was saying that if our bodies are a garden, it takes a LOT of willpower to be a good gardener and to look after ourselves properly.

Let's try and plant some healthy habits!

All of the activities in this book can help to reduce stress, make you feel calmer, happier and more in control, which in turn makes you healthier. But the opposite is true too – being healthy in itself also helps to keep you happy.

Tracking your health habits can help you work out if you need to make any changes.

Activity: Create a health tracker

Ask yourself these questions and see how your health habits measure up!

How much SLEEP do you get each night?
10 to 11 hours for 6 to 9 year olds
9 to 10 hours for 9 to 13 year olds

How much WATER do you drink each day?
5 glasses (1 litre) for 6 to 8 year olds
7 glasses (1.5 litres) for 9 to 12 year olds
8 to 10 glasses (2 litres) for 13+ years

How many portions of FRUIT and VEG do you eat each day? UK experts say we should all eat at least five portions a day, but it's okay to have more! A portion is the amount you can hold in the palm of your hand. How many do you get?

How many sweet TREATS do you have each day? Experts say we should have no more than two small sugary treats a day — that includes drinks, cakes, biscuits and sweets. How many did you have today?

How much EXERCISE do you get each day? Experts say young people should get at least an hour a day. This can include walking to school, sport, PE lessons and being active.

Starting from the left side of the graph on the next page tick off the number of happy circles that match the number of each activities you do in a typical day.

sleep

water

fruit + veg.

treats

exercise

So how did it go?

How did you measure up? Was today an average day? Do you have healthy habits? Do you need to make any changes?

How it works

Research shows that people's health behaviours tend to mirror those of their family and friends. Invite them to join you, support you, and help you stay on track!

Create your own happy...

...by making your own tracker using graph paper and seeing how healthy your habits are over a week or month. Tracking your habits can be a great way to properly measure what you do. Once you know this you can easily make small changes that will help you become more healthy.

18. Stay Happy Online

The internet has been a boon and a curse for teenagers.
– JK Rowling (Author of 'Harry Potter')

Do you agree Do you think the internet is an invention which has benefits but also causes problems?

It can be great to find new information, giggle at cat videos, always have music at our fingertips, to play games, follow favourite YouTubers and to keep up with friends.

But the internet can be a tricky thing too. It can take up a lot of time, people can hide behind their profiles and be lots meaner than they would in real life and bad people can pretend to be children. Comparing ourselves to what others share of their lives online can make us feel down.

How do you stay happy online?

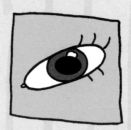 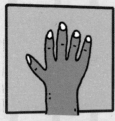 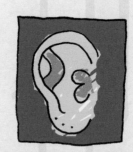

How do you feel when you use the internet?

What words would you use to describe how you feel about the internet? Write them in the empty clouds. Feel free to use the words on the big cloud or make up your own.

SAD
relaxed inspired
tired bored happy
amused stressed
anxious
in control

Here are some ways
to Create Your Own Happy Internet:

Stand up against Cyberbullies

If someone sends you hurtful messages, puts you
down, harasses you, threatens you, sends other
people nasty messages pretending to be you,
gets other people to act against you or tries to get
you to do something you don't want to do, that
is cyberbullying. It can happen in texts, on social
media, in chat rooms and on gaming networks. It
is WRONG and can make you very UNHAPPY. If this
is happening to you or someone you know, tell an
adult. You don't have to put up with it.

Spread kindness

Just as you would offline you can share
compliments, kind words, acts of kindness and
happy things. Happiness spreads through social
networks like a good virus. It's always worth
remembering that people can't see your face or
hear your voice so you have to work extra hard
online to make sure your words sound kind.

Learn new skills

Learning new things keeps us happy!

- Use YouTube videos to learn a dance routine
- Create a playlist of happy tunes
- Learn to play an instrument
- Improve your art skills
- Learn STEM skills — coding, science experiments, inventing...
- Learn some words from another language

Just Be Yourself

If you use social media, choose to be on the platforms that make you truly happy. Remember that your profile and the way you use it doesn't have to be the same as everyone else's. You don't have to post endless selfies or always share what you have been up to – oversharing or trying to be the same as other people can be very tiring. Also keep in mind that once you post something online, you have no control over who sees it, even if you think you're only sharing it with your friends. So don't share anything secret, or your address or phone number.

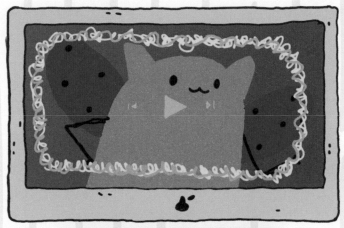

Find your niche, find your tribe

Some people have a NICHE, one subject that they love to talk about on the internet such as pets, gaming, baking, crafting, nature or other hobbies. This is a great way to find your TRIBE without having to share everything.

Spread the happiness

As you would in real life, surround yourself with the people who make you feel positive. Researchers found a 'three degrees of connection happiness benefit'. This means there is a connection between your happiness online and your friends' happiness online, AS WELL as between your happiness and your friends' friends' friends' happiness.

So how did it go?

How do you feel about your use of the internet? Is there anything you would like to change? How could you make the internet a happier place?

How it works

It's true, the internet can be a boon and a curse! Lots of researchers have found that the internet can make us more stressed and depressed, because we compare ourselves to others. It can also be addictive. But some researchers have also found it gives us a sense of freedom and control, which has a positive impact on our happiness.

Create your own happy...

...by being careful about how you spend your time, how the internet makes you feel and how the people around you make you feel. Remember to tell an adult if something doesn't feel right. And keep learning new stuff!

Spread the happy

Happiness is like jam, you can't spread even a little without getting some on yourself – Author unknown

When you have done all the activities in Part 1, you will be so full of happy that it will just ooze out of you. You will be like a bucket that overflows when it is full of water.

Happiness is something you cannot help but share – it is as contagious as a smile. When you are full of happy, it is easy to be kind and encouraging, sharing and full of cheer. By helping just one other person feel happier the chances are that they, in turn, will spread that happiness to others, and so on and so on. You will start a whole wave of happiness which will spread far and wide.

After you've made someone else happy, you will find that the feeling of making them happy has made you even happier too. So never doubt how much impact your one small action can have.

Always make sure your happy tank is kept topped up so it can overflow! You and your happy are a very powerful force.

HAPPY!

How it works

Studies show that when you are kind and helpful and giving and try to make other people feel happy the mesolimbic system (the bit of the brain responsible for feelings of reward) is triggered. When you help others be happier your brain releases feel-good chemicals and these will encourage you to to be even more helpful and kind as well as feel super happy yourself. Everyone wins!

Making others happy is an awesome thing to do! This section is full of ideas to help you do just that.

1. Say Thank You

Feeling gratitude and not expressing it is like wrapping a present and not giving it.
> – William Arthur Ward (Writer and poet)

We experience gratitude when we look for things to be thankful for. Being grateful is important but doing something with our gratitude is even more important. Gratitude can be an action as well as a feeling and when we express it, it can have HUGELY positive effects on us and on the people we thank.

Activity: Tree of gratitude

Okay, we are setting you a mission. Find two people to thank. When you thank them, also tell them what you are thankful for. Choose one person from your friends or family, and make the second person someone who has helped you, such as a bus driver or a teacher.

Ready, steady... ...GO!

Who did you choose and what did they do to make you want to say thank you to them?

Write each of their names on a separate leaf from the happy tree below. Each time you say thank you to someone new remember to come back and fill in a leaf. You'll soon fill it up with an array of names of wonderful people who you are grateful to.

So how did it go?

Did you get a warm and happy feeling inside?
Were you nervous? What did they say back to you?

How it works

80% of parents think learning to say please
and thank you are the most important skills
their children could learn. Robert A. Emmons,
a psychology professor at the University of
California, has shown that as well as keeping
parents happy, people who regularly show
gratitude are definitely a lot happier, healthier and
have more friends than those who don't. How cool
is that! In fact there are just SO many benefits to
being thankful.

Create your own happy...

...by making gratitude your new thing. Always
deliver your thank you with a big smile –
you will definitely get one back.

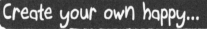

2. Stand up for others

Strong people stand up for themselves.
But the strongest people stand up for others

– Unknown Author

Many children experience bullying so there is a chance you have seen it or that it has even happened to you. If you do see it, you can take action without having to get into a fight. Tell someone. Being bullied is horrible and can affect people for their whole lives.

Next time you see someone being left out, teased, picked on or pushed around, tell an adult you trust, like a teacher or a guide/scout leader. You can do this in private. Bullying often stops when it is reported, which means that YOU can make a big difference.

Activity: Help to stop bullying

Can you name three people you trust to tell if you know someone is being bullied? Draw their faces on the next page and add their names or titles under your drawings.

colour me!

84

We know it can be hard to tell on people, but it is ALWAYS the right thing to do if they are bullying someone. Knowing who to tell makes this easier.

Some things in life are pretty simple, like saying thank you, and they bring instant happy results. Some things can feel uncomfortable but when we have done them we feel glad.

How do you think people feel when they are bullied? Pop any words that spring to mind into the thought bubble below.

So how did it go?

Could you easily think of three people you trust? This is important because these are the people you can and should go to for help. And (count them up!) how many bad feelings ended up in your thought bubble? This is the amount of bad feelings you can heal by helping to stop bullying.

How it works

Bullying isn't just a bit of harmless fun amongst children; it can affect people's health, work and relationships as they grow up. By telling someone about the bullying, we can help to stop it. And if we help stop people from bullying others when they are younger, they might not become bullies when they are adults.

Create your own happy...

...by telling an adult you trust about the bullying, and doing something to stop it. It is important not to be a bystander and do nothing. Use the power you have to not join in with the bullying and to be part of the solution.

If you don't feel you can tell a teacher, tell the most sensible and caring adult you know.

3. Make friends with an older person

You can make more friends in two months by becoming interested in other people than you can in two years by trying to get other people interested in you. — Dale Carnegie (Author)

Age UK is a charity for older people in the UK and they say over one million older people haven't spoken to a friend, neighbour or family member for at least a month. That is so sad.

We need to look out for older neighbours and relatives that have no one visiting them. Does that sound boring? I promise you it's not. I once listened to my neighbour, who was 96, all afternoon about being captured in the war and escaping from a prisoner of war camp. He was fascinating! We all have stories to tell...

You might have grandparents you love very much but do you ever talk to them? I don't mean just tell them about what you have done, what I mean is talk to them about what they do all day, where they have been, or what their childhood was like.

Activity: Make an older friend

Cheer up an older person you know by doing one of these:

- Ask them some questions about their life — about their first car, first job, or what their school was like

- Ask your grandparents if you can look through their old photo albums with them — you may uncover a wealth of family secrets!

- If you have an older neighbour who seems lonely, pop round with an adult and take them some cake and just say Hi.

Make some notes about their stories below.

So how did it go?

Was becoming friends with an older person more fun than you were expecting? Did you hear some interesting stories? Are you keen to find out more?

How it works

Research has shown that loneliness is as bad for someone's health as smoking fifteen cigarettes a day, and is worse for them than being obese.

You can help change that!

One of the benefits of living a really long time is that they will have probably done and seen a whole lot of things, met many people, lived through a war and seen new things invented. I bet they have some great stories to tell you.

Create your own happy...

...by befriending an older person and listening to their fabulous tales of long ago, you will make them feel happier and be healthier too!

4. Be a really good friend

A friend is one of the nicest things you can have and one of the best things you can be.
— AA Milne (Author of 'Winnie The Pooh')

To have a good friend you have to be one. And in order to be one you have to really understand the qualities that people want in a friend and then try and behave that way yourself.

You need to be the friend you want to have.
It all starts with you.

Activity: Friendship qualities

Your friendship is a gift so what will you put inside?

MY FRIEndShip.

Imagine filling your gift box with five qualities that make a good friend. Draw or write these qualities in five of the boxes below. Then ask five different people for one word which is important to them in a friendship and add those in the remaining boxes.

So how did it go?

Do you feel you know more now about what being a good friend involves? Can you put this into action?

How it works

Having friends can literally kill your pain! Scientists believe that when we see our friends endorphins are released in the brain, which make us feel happy. Endorphins are also powerful painkillers and so it is believed that having close friendships may actually prove to be better than the strongest pain-killing medicine you can take! How cool is that?

Create your own happy...

...by being a good friend – you will make other people feel fabulous and receive so much back in return.

5. Random acts of kindness

No act of kindness, however small, is ever wasted
— **Aesop (Greek fabulist and storyteller)**

A random act of kindness is basically an act of kindness done for no particular reason or reward. You can do these for people you do or don't know.

Activity: Be kind

On the next page there are lots of lovely ideas for random acts of kindness. Simply spin a penny on that page every once in a while and follow the instructions for the RAOK you land on until you have done them all. Colour each one as you go so that you can remember which ones you have done.

GIVE SOMEONE
YOU KNOW
A HUG

MAKE
SOMEONE
LAUGH

TAKE SOME
PET FOOD to
A LOCAL SHELTER

DONATE
to A
CHARITY

FEED
THE
BIRDS

GIVE
SOMEONE
A
COMPLIMENT

MAKE
SOMEONE A
GIFT

GIVE
SOMEONE
FLOWERS

HELP do
THE
CHORES

So how did it go?

How did it feel to be so kind? Were you awkward/embarrassed/happy? What response did you get?

How it works

The Random Acts of Kindness Foundation has discovered that carrying out random kind acts will:

- Reduce depression: Thinking about helping other people stops us worrying about ourselves
- Reduce pain: Helping releases endorphins, which are natural painkillers
- Reduce isolation: Helping others encourages human contact
- Reduce blood pressure
- Reduce anxiety: Good actions can lift mood and decrease social avoidance
- Reduce stress: Kind people have twenty-three percent less cortisol (the stress hormone) and age more slowly

Wow, it's SO good for you to make other people happy!

Create your own happy...

...by being kind whenever possible and constantly thinking up new and imaginative ways to do this.

6. Give compliments

One compliment can keep me going for a whole month.
— Mark Twain (Author)

Compliments are little gifts of love. They can be about someone's personality, actions, looks or just about anything.

Everyone loves to be complimented (even if they do get a little embarrassed). It makes them feel valued and appreciated and most definitely HAPPY.

Activity: Be complimentary

Can you give someone one of these compliments today? How about aiming to give out two every day for the next week!

If saying them feels awkward, why not just snip off one of the slips on the next page and hand it out.

You make me laugh so much

You are so kind

I love spending time with you

You are so smart

I always enjoy your company

I AM SO PROUD OF YOU

YOU HAVE THE BEST SMILE

You did so well today

What a great cook you are

I LOVE BEING YOUR FRIEND

Compliments work really well if you add detail, e.g. 'You are so kind – I loved it when you shared your cake with me.' So do try and add the WHY bit if you can. You could also suggest to your teacher that you try this activity in your class.

So how did it go?

Were you or they awkward about the compliment? Do you think it made them happy? Did it get easier the more compliments you gave?

How it works

Researchers have found that to the brain, receiving a compliment is as much a social reward as being given money. Focusing on and noticing the good qualities in the world around us gives our moods a boost all by itself.

Create your own happy...

...by giving compliments regularly. The more you give, the easier it is and the more you will focus on good things about other people. As with all things, you will get what you give, and getting compliments will make you feel happier too.

7. Snail Mail

To send a letter is a good way to go somewhere without moving anything but your heart.
   – Phyllis Theroux (Essayist, author and teacher)

Do you even know what snail mail is? It's mail that comes through the post, like a letter or a postcard. It's called snail mail because unlike email or texting it takes a while to get there.

Activity: Send someone a letter

Decide first of all who you think might love
to hear from you then simply get started.
Here are a list of things to include.
Give each one a tick as you use it.

- Use your best writing, so it's easy
  for them to read
- Put your address on the top of your letter so
  they can write back to you
- Put the date on it — lots of people keep letters
  and love to recall when they were sent
- Ask a few questions such as: How are you?
  and How was your holiday/birthday?
- Tell them what you have been up to
- Tell them what you have coming up
  (e.g. holiday, exams)
- Sign off by wishing them something lovely
  — like a happy day or great summer
- Address your envelope. You could decorate it too
  — it would make the postal workers happy as well
  as the letter receiver
- Pop on a stamp
- Post! (So many letters never get posted.)
- Maybe you could include a small token like
  a photo or friendship bracelet, a recipe
  or a drawing

So how did it go?

Did you find it easy to write a letter
rather than sending an email or text?
How did you feel when you posted it?

How it works

Receiving letters/postcards is much more personal
than email, as you see the person's handwriting
and it shows that they went out of their way.
It makes people SO happy to receive snail mail.
They know it has taken someone time and effort
and they feel cared for and thought about.
Lots of people keep letters and re-read them too.

Create your own happy...

...by being an awesome letter writer and spreading
your happy vibes far and wide. You could also ask
your parents if any of their old friends have kids
your age who might like a pen pal.

It can be fabulous to send letters and to receive
them is EVEN BETTER.

8. Encourage Someone

We rise by lifting others
          – Robert G. Ingersoll (Politician and lawyer)

Isn't it lovely to be supported and encouraged by people who care? It is important that we are someone who offers such support and encouragement to others when they need it too.

Activity: Be someone's cheerleader

Try and think of one thing you could DO and one thing you could SAY to be encouraging in each of the situations below:

1. Your friend is about to move to a new town. They are worried about making new friends and sad about leaving behind their old ones. How could you encourage them?
(Even if you feel sad about them leaving too.)

_____

_____

_____

_____

_____

2. Your older cousin has to learn lines for the school play and they are struggling. How could you encourage them?

_____

_____

_____

_____

_____

3. A younger child in the playground is trying to learn to skip but keeps stumbling and yet their friends can all do it easily. How could you encourage them?

_____

_____

_____

_____

_____

_____

_____

So how did it go?

How did they react to your encouragement? Do you think it made a difference to how well they did?

How it works

Scientists have found that emotions like fear, anxiety and anger affect our concentration and as a result we don't perform as well when we feel them. When we're feeling upbeat and happy, we are more likely to perform better. So with the help of someone encouraging us, speaking positively to us and helping us come up with a plan, we will feel more positive and as a result do things better!

Create your own happy...

...by being the VERY best of cheerleaders – one that helps other people feel positive and achieve to the best of their ability. It will make you feel so good to be part of their success too, you'll both be happier. If you see someone struggling always try and think what you can do or say to encourage them.

9. Be an includer

We are all different, which is great because we are all unique. Without diversity life would be very boring.
— Catherine Pulsifer (Motivational writer)

We are all different in so many ways and whilst this is a MARVELLOUS thing it can also lead to people being left out, made fun of, or ignored. They might be left out because of the colour of their skin or hair, how they look, a disability, their unusual way of thinking or communicating, how they dress, or any manner of reasons. Sometime it's not obvious why someone is being left out – they just are.

Obviously it's a really horrible experience for anyone not to be included, and can make them feel lonely and unhappy. So what can we do ... how can we be 'inclusive', ensuring no one is purposefully left out?

You have to be brave to reach out of your comfort zone, but new friends make life MUCH more interesting. Just think how much happier you are potentially going to make that person.

Activity: Include someone

Think for a minute about a time you were left out and how that felt. Now realize you have the power to stop that for someone else.

So who can you think of in your life who regularly seems to be left out? What could you do to help?

Here are a whole host of tips to set you thinking.

- Challenge unkind comments about a left-out child and let other people know it is not okay to exclude someone.
- Look for something you have in common with a left-out child. We are all much more alike than we ever realize and people will always surprise you.
- Include the left-out child at lunch time — sit with them or ask them to sit with you.
- Recruit a friend to your inclusiveness mission — it is always easier with two.
- Be flexible — if a child is a wheelchair user and you are playing football while they watch from the sidelines, could you ask them if there is a sport they like playing and set that up next break.
- Get educated — if a child in your class uses an alternative method of communication, such as sign language, learn how that works so you can engage with them. Ask your teacher for help.

your space
to write

Now you have your Inclusion Plan, you just need
to put it into action!

So how did it go?

Did it work? What effect did it have on the other person? Would you do it again? Would you try something different next time?

How it works

Being excluded may not leave external scars, but according to psychology professors it can cause pain that is deeper and lasts longer than a physical injury. By including someone who is left out, we can make a HUGE difference to how they feel.

Create your own happy...

...by being aware of those left out and making it your mission to help them feel part of what is going on. Find out if your school has Inclusion Ambassadors, who work to stop children being left out.

10. The Habit of Compassion

All through this chapter we have thought about ways we can make other people happy and in the process make ourselves happy. In the end it is really all about compassion - and making it a habit.

If you want others to be happy, practice compassion. If you want to be happy, practice compassion.
                    – Dalai Lama (Spiritual leader)

The definition of compassion is a strong feeling of sympathy and concern for the suffering or bad luck of others and a wish to help them. It can help other people feel much happier if we act with compassion towards them.

Activity:

The first step towards being a compassionate person is recognising what makes people sad. In the teardrop on the next page, write a list of things BIG and SMALL which could make others unhappy.

write in teardrop

The next page has nine frames and each one represents a chance to be compassionate. Colour in a frame each time you are compassionate. Use the following colours:

- If you HELP someone, use red
- If you LISTEN to someone's troubles, use blue
- If you SAY something supportive, use green
- If you VOLUNTEER for a charity, use yellow
- If you DO anything else, use purple

Cut the page out and stick it on your fridge
if it will help you to remember.

So how did it go?

Did being compassionate become a habit? Did you find yourself looking for ways to help? How long did it take to fill in your frames and how did it feel to colour them all in?

How it works

Buddhists believe there is a real difference between the temporary happiness of getting what we want and the real happiness of leading a meaningful, compassionate life. Scientists believe that living a compassionate lifestyle make us feel good because in our brains the act of giving appears to be as pleasurable as the act of receiving, if not more so.

Create your own happy...

...by getting into the habit of being compassionate.

colour me!

Are you ready to make a happier world?

The people who are crazy enough to think they can change the world, are the ones who do.
  — Advertising campaign for Apple Inc.

All of the activities in this section have the power to make you feel happier, but they also have HAPPY side effects for the whole world.

Whether you love looking after animals, nature, the planet, fundraising, supporting a cause or are just curious to find out what REALLY matters to you, Part 3 is all about THE BIG STUFF.

It's messy, it's fun, it's creative, it's wild and it's wonderful.

Time to get out there and make your happy mark on the world!

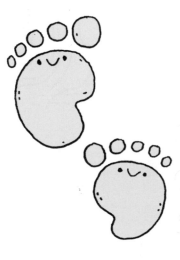

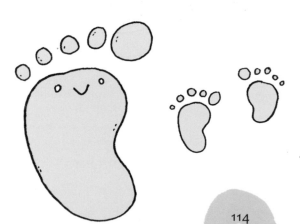

The Butterfly Effect

The 'butterfly effect' is a scientific theory that a single event, no matter how small, can change the course of the universe forever.

So in the weather system, the movement of a butterfly beating its wings could cause a tornado somewhere else. That's hard to imagine isn't it?

Let's try another example!

In human terms, this means our small actions can have MUCH BIGGER effects further down the line...

Here are some young people who started butterfly-wing small but changed the world!

7-year-old Jacob Rabi-Laleh, from Essex, made a poster asking for donations for the homeless. His whole town joined in until his garden was filled with rucksacks full of stuff. Lots of people saw the video the BBC made about him and decided to help the homeless too. Imagine all the lives he has changed.

Malala Yousafzai, from Pakistan, started writing for the BBC Urdu service about her concerns about the Taliban political movement not letting girls go to school. She was shot in the head on her way home from school by members of the Taliban in 2013 and survived. There were protests across Pakistan and people across the world came to her support. Millions signed a petition which led to Pakistan's first Right To Free and Compulsory Education Bill. She became the youngest recipient of a Nobel Peace Prize in 2014.

Easton LaChappelle, from America, made his first robotic hand at the age of 14, using LEGO and fishing wire. He made it his mission to design affordable prosthetic limbs. NASA were so impressed they asked him to work on their Robonaut team.

Mary Grace Henry, from America, was only 12 when she asked for a sewing machine for her birthday and taught herself how to make reversible headbands to sell at school. She made enough to pay for a girl's education in another country. She has since made thousands of hair accessories and sent sixty-six girls in Kenya, Uganda, Paraguay and Haiti to school, and created the 'Reverse The Course' organisation.

This section is full of activities that could start a ripple that could end up changing the world.

1. Reduce, reuse, recycle

Reusing and recycling our materials are the most important things we can do. - Nikki Reed (Actress)

It's easy to think that the packaging we buy can be recycled, and that we are being green when we put it into the recycling bin. But what if we could reduce the things we put into the recycling? This would mean fewer trucks to move our rubbish, less energy to recycle it and less packaging in the first place.

Did you know reducing waste can actually make us happy? Explore your family's recycling, take some steps to reduce the amount of rubbish you create and reuse recyclables to make a scary but lovable reminder to reduce your waste!

Activity: Make a recycling monster

Our family talks a lot about reducing waste, but it wasn't until we made a recycling monster that we really began to talk about how we could reduce our own recycling pile. Sometimes you have to come face to face with the recycling monster!

1. Assemble the materials and your family

2. Create your own recycling monster, sticking boxes and packets together with masking tape and then painting your creation

3. As you create your monster, talk about what you could do to reduce the amount of waste you create each week.

Can you find an alternative with less packaging?

Can you make cakes or biscuits instead of buying them in boxes or plastic containers?

Could you make pizza dough instead of buying takeaway or ready-made pizzas?

Can you get milk delivered in reusable glass bottles, instead of buying it in plastic bottles from the supermarket?

Can you find someone locally who keeps chickens who could use egg boxes?

Can you use both sides of pieces of paper, or use scrap paper for shopping lists?

4. Display your monster somewhere, to remind you all to think about reducing waste.

You could also create a monster on the beach with all the rubbish that drifts onto the shore. It would make a brilliant reminder that we should take our rubbish home with us.

Rubbish becoming art, making a statement and helping to change the world!

So how did it go?

What ideas to reduce waste did you come up with? Were you surprised by how much rubbish you had made in a week?

How it works

We're starting slowly to realize that having less can actually make us happier than having more! Plus research is also showing a connection between caring for our world and being happier people. The European Social Survey questioned 50,000 people from thirty nations. People who agree with the statement 'It is important to care for the environment' also reported being happier.

Create your own happy...

...by seeing if you can take on a Zero Waste challenge? Could you create zero recycling or rubbish in a week? Imagine the impact if we could all do this? Several families in Denmark took part in a Zero Waste challenge, and reported they had felt more happiness during the experiment!

2. Grow Your Own Happy

The best time to plant a tree was twenty years ago.
The second best time is now. – Chinese proverb

Trees take a long time to grow but it is great fun to grow alongside them. If you have room for a tree as the proverb says, plant one now! But if not there are so many things that you can grow that will not only bring you happy vibes, but also help the planet too.

Food grown at home can be cheaper, travels less food miles, and usually has more nutrients. You can also decide what pesticides to use or not use. Homegrown usually tastes better too and is fresher.

Learning to grow your own is fun and a great skill for a happy, healthy life and you don't need to have a garden to grow things. Many plants will happily thrive indoors. Peppers will happily grow anywhere they get a little sun, while plants like aloe vera will survive even in quite dark corners as long as they get a little watering!

Activity: Get growing!

The trick with growing your own is to start small and keep it manageable. Plant things you love and you will enjoy looking after them. Here are some ideas:

Cress Heads. Clean out old egg shells and draw faces on them, fill with damp cotton wool and sprinkle on your cress seeds.

Lettuce and Herbs. These are easy to grow in pots and you can keep going back and cutting them as you need them. Lettuce is great in salads and herbs add flavour to food.

Super Spuds. Growing your own potatoes and digging them up is really satisfying. Potatoes are easy to grow. If you don't have a big garden you can grow them in special bags.

Power Peas. Peas never make it into our pans, because we always eat them straight from the pod. They are easy to plant but do need some canes to grow up, and make a lovely vitamin rich snack!

Awesome Apple Tree. If you have room for a tree, apple trees are really rewarding producing lots of fruit in the late summer and early autumn.

So how did it go?

What have you decided to plant and why?
Did your plants grow? How did they taste?

How it works

Texas A&M University found
that people who spend time
around plants and nature
are more likely to be kinder
to others. People who have
flowers are more likely to be
happier, because flowers
improve our mood and make
us feel more positive.
Gardening improves our
concentration and memory
and helps us deal with stress.

Create your own happy...

...by learning to grow your own, it's a brilliant life
skill but it takes a bit of time and patience. You
also have to accept that even the most experienced
gardener's crops fail sometimes. Don't be afraid to
ask for help and advice and just think how many
things you will be able to grow as an adult if you
master a new crop each year now!

3. Be a Happiness Philosopher

Happiness depends upon ourselves
            –Aristotle (Ancient Greek philosopher)

Philosophy basically means trying to understand the meaning of life. Philosophers asks questions to understand how and why people do certain things and how to live a happy life. Big questions like... Why are humans here? How should we treat ourselves, each other and our world?

This book is jam packed full of ideas and scientific research about what makes happiness. This chapter takes this a stage further: it is time to become a happiness philosopher yourself!

Activity: Become a happiness philosopher

Here are some big questions to start you off as a happiness philosopher. You could discuss them with family and friends – philosophical discussion is great for helping you push your ideas further. Why not discuss one at mealtimes each day this week?

DOES HAPPINESS DEPEND ON OURSELVES?

- Can we make our own happiness?
- How much can we control?
- How much do others control?
- Can we stop others making us unhappy?

CAN ONE PERSON CHANGE THE WORLD?

- Can you think of people who have changed the world by their actions?
- Can little actions change the world?
- Can you think of a situation where you have changed the world?
- Can kindness change the world?

THE AWARD FOR
hAppiNEss philosophER
goes to

YOUR NAME

CAN YOU THINK YOURSELF HAPPY?

- If you focus on happy things does it make you happier?
- Does thinking about your happiness make you happier?

ARE THE BEST THINGS IN LIFE FREE?

- What can you think of in life that is free that makes you happy?
- What costs money?
- Is there any difference in how happy they make you?
- Does money always make people happier?
- Is there a perfect amount of money that makes people happiest?

HOW SHOULD WE TREAT ANIMALS?

- What are the differences between animals and humans?
- What makes animals happy?
- What do animals understand?
- How should humans treat animals?

So how did it go?

Did your ideas change the more questions you asked? Can you think of any more happiness philosophy questions?

How it works

Asking questions and thinking about problems from different points of view helps us to solve them with kindness. Researchers at Durham University found that children who learnt philosophy at school had better social and communication skills, teamwork, resilience and empathy. They also did better in tests!

Create your own happy...

...by keeping on asking questions and having discussions. When we are young we naturally ask questions, but as we grow up we forget to – stay curious and stay happy!

4. Upcycling

Upcycling is taking an item that is no longer needed or wanted and giving it new life as something that is either useful or creative. — Upcycling Magazine

As well as being good for the environment (which it really is) it is also really good fun to make something new out of something old.

My grandad had an old tea cosy and when he got a new one rather than throw the old one away away he put a patch on the spout hole and made it into a hat! What a brilliant upcycle and a very unusual-looking hat! Fortunately, as people try to use less and preserve the resources we have, upcycling has become much more fashionable than my Grandad's hat!

Activity: Make something marvellous!

We want to give you absolutely free reign over what your upcycling project is because we know just how fabulously creative you are! Upcycling is all about your imagination and creativity so here are some ideas. We absolutely can't wait to hear about your creation.

CUT DOWN
old jeans to make shorts and maybe add some funky patches

other ideas

SPRAY
paint a muffin pan silver and use it to store your jewellery or stationery

MAKE
brilliant new multi-coloured crayons by breaking up old ones into a silicone mould and baking them until they melt

WRAP
an old tin can in coloured paper and draw on a cute face for a lovely pen pot

PAINT
an old plant pot a really bright colour, stick some shells on it and pop in a bulb

UPCYCLE
an old jam jar by sticking lace around it and filling it with sweets

- My upcycling project....
- Materials I need....
- How to make it .....

BE SAFE

Be safe: sharp edges, spray paint, glue, hot ovens and rusty nails can all be dangerous - do use your smarts and have an adult check over your project with you and help with any safety concerns.

You can stick in a photo or a drawing of your finished project here...

So how did it go?

Was it fun? Was it tricky?
Were you proud of your creation?

How it works

Researchers say upcycling rocks because it helps the environment in lots of brilliant ways:

- It stops old things going into landfill sites, where a gas called methane is released, which contributes to climate change.

- When you upcycle there is is no need for recycling which, despite being better than just chucking something, still uses up energy and resources.

Create your own happy...

...by making use of old items, which might save you buying new things. It also cuts down on new things having to be made, which is better for the environment. Being creative and solving problems is good for your happiness. Who knows you might come up with a great idea and change the world like Mary Grace Henry!

There are just so many benefits to upcycling!

5. Make a home for a wild animal

Nature is not a place to visit. It is home.
— Gary Snyder (Poet)

Research shows us that being in nature makes us happier, and that many wild animals are losing their homes. Can you help make a home for a wild creature, and make yourself happier in the process?

Activity: Be a homemaker

Easy - Hedgehog Home

A pile of leaves and some logs is all a hedgehog needs to get settled. Look for a quiet corner in the garden or park, where it won't be disturbed. Pile up the logs and branches to make a cosy shelter and fill with leaves. Even if you don't attract a hedgehog, insects and newts will also love this kind of set-up.

Medium - Insect Hotel

First, create the hotel structure in a sunny or part-shaded site that won't be disturbed. Use bricks or stones to make a base, then add wooden planks or old roof tiles to create floors. An old roof tile makes a perfect roof to keep the hotel dry too.

Next, create the rooms by tucking old flower pots into the gaps or using stones to divide the floors up.

Finally, add the bedding. Different guests will like different things, here are some ideas:

- Dead wood and loose bark are perfect for beetles, centipedes, spiders and woodlice
- Bamboo and reeds with hollow centres are great for bees
- Frogs loves larger, damp holes with stones and tiles
- Ladybird guests like dry leaves, sticks or straw
- Corrugated cardboard is perfect for lacewing

You could also use pine cones, moss or whatever else you can find in the garden.

Challenge - Birdhouse

You can make a birdhouse using off-cuts of wood if an adult is around to help. Try downloading a template from the internet to turn a single plank into a bird box. It doesn't need to be perfect, birds don't mind as long as it is warm and dry. You will need to hinge one panel so you can clean it out. The hole needs to be about 25 mm for blue, coal and marsh tits. Robins and wrens prefer an open front panel.

So how did it go?

What did you make and did anything move in? Don't be too disappointed if nothing moves in straight away, animals can take time to find the perfect home, just like humans!

Notice the effect being in nature has on you – does it calm you? Inspire you? Excite you? Scare you?

How it works

Have you heard of the '30 Days Wild' campaign where people sign up to do something in nature every day throughout June? Well, the University of Derby and The Wildlife Trusts measured the people who took part one year and found a scientific increase in their happiness and health for months later! Children who took part said it boosted their self-esteem and happiness, made them calmer, and let them take risks and learn more.

Create your own happy...

...by looking out for other ways to encourage even more nature into your garden or local spaces.

6. Awe Moments

We are just an advanced breed of monkeys on a minor planet of a very average star. But we can understand the universe. That makes us something very special.

– Stephen Hawking (Theoretical physicist & cosmologist)

Stephen Hawking was spot on, understanding our universe makes humans special, but did you know taking time to really notice the universe can make you happier and kinder too? Experiencing awe – a feeling of wonder and amazement – is scientifically proven to make us kinder. Here is an exercise that can help you feel in awe wherever you are.

Activity: Be at one with the world

Cloud pictures – Lie down and spend five minutes watching the clouds. Take some deep breaths, let your mind relax and see what pictures you can see in the clouds. Animals? People? Stories? If you want to learn more about cloud formations you could look up the different types of clouds. This is a brilliant activity for long car journeys. Bring some awe to your whole family.

Stargaze – Learn how to identify some stars, using a book, an adult or an app for help. The Plough is an easy group to spot, it's made up of seven stars that, joined together, look a lot like a saucepan. Sometimes the saucepan appears upside down because it spins round the North Star every 24 hours as the Earth rotates.

It's close to the Celestial North Pole (that is a point in the sky directly above the North Pole), meaning it's always visible in the night sky. You could use a compass to get your feet facing north.

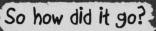
So how did it go?

How does it make you feel when you look at the clouds or the stars?

How it works

Happiness comes from appreciating the everyday moments and seeing the world with new eyes.

Cloud spotting and stargazing can give us a very different perspective on the world. Sometimes seeing how big the world is can actually make our own problems feel smaller too.

Researchers at the University of California-Irvine found that when we experience awe we are more likely to be kind, cooperative and to help others. Isn't that awe-inspiring?

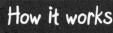
Create your own happy...

...by taking a few minutes each day to seek out an awe moment. Encourage others to join you. Wherever you are in the world you can always find some calm and perspective by looking at clouds and stars.

7. Create New Life

We may think we are nurturing our garden, but of course it's our garden that is really nurturing us.
— Jenny Uglow (Writer)

Are you ready for a secret mission?

Seeds bombs are a fun and peaceful way to bring life and colour back to gloomy patches of land.

The best time to drop them is spring or autumn, and timing your blasts around rainfall will help the seeds to get off to a good start. It's fun to choose areas you will walk past regularly, so you can keep an eye on the results.

Activity: Make a seed bomb

You will need:

- Flower seed
- Potter's clay powder, from any craft shop.
- Peat-free compost
- Water
- A bowl
- A baking tray

Mix the seed, clay, and compost together in a bowl to a ratio of three handfuls of clay, five handfuls of compost and one handful of seed. Carefully add the water a little bit at a time, mixing it all together until you get a consistency that you can form into small balls. Lay them out to bake dry on a sunny windowsill for at least three hours.

It's worth asking an adult where a good place to drop your seed bombs would be, whether it's your own garden, a neglected flower bed along your street, a long-forgotten planter, or a patch of wasteland.

CREATE NEW LIFE BY DROPPING A seed bomb!

clay   seeds   compost   water

So how did it go?

Was it fun to make? Where did you throw
your bombs?

How it works

In the wild, seeds can be spread by wind, water
and animals who like to eat them and then poo
them out somewhere else. By making a seed
bomb you are helping seeds along their journey –
without having to do it the way animals do it!

Create your own happy...

...by creating something so beautiful you will be
bursting with pride! Go seed bombing with friends
and family and then make a date to go back and
see if your seeds grew. If you want to get into
gardening a bit more, why not check whether
there are any community gardening projects
in your local area and volunteer to help out?

8. Find Happiness in Trees

Trees are poems that the earth writes upon the sky.
— Kahlil Gibran (Writer, poet and artist)

The Japanese invented *Shinrin-yoku* ('forest bathing'), and now scientists have proved it really works! Scientists say that just looking at trees can make us happier. Serotonin is the name for the chemical in our bodies that keeps us happy. Being in nature gives this serotonin a boost to make us feel happier.

Making a 'nature photograph' is a great way to tell the story of an outdoor adventure, and bring nature inside for a serotonin boost.

Activity: Make a nature photograph
You will need:

- A postcard-sized piece of coloured card
- Double-sided sticky tape
- A forest, wood, park or anywhere nature is growing

Put a strip of double-sided sticky tape across the middle of one side of your piece of card and take it out with you for a nature walk.

143

Pick things up as you go and stick them on your card. Try looking for different colours, textures, shapes and sizes, from tiny seeds to bits of bark, leaves and flowers.

You can arrange them on the card to make an interesting picture or pattern.

You could make one for each season and put them together to create a forest photograph gallery.

So how did it go?

Circle three words to describe how you felt on your walk, or when you look at your picture.

calm
peaceful dreamy
joyful surprised curious
relaxed thoughtful
excited

Did you feel any other feelings? You could write them down too.

How it works

When a group of scientists at the University of Chicago tracked people's happiness for seventeen years, they found that the people were happiest when they were living near trees, while in Pennsylvania, hospital patients with a view of trees went home on average a day earlier than people with no view. In Japan, researchers found that a one-day trip to a park can boost our 'natural killer' white blood cells and proteins that help to fight off illness for at least seven days afterwards. Being in trees makes us much healthier.

Create your own happy...

...by getting out in nature, looking at trees, walking near trees and running through trees. This will make you healthy AND happy!

9. Feed the birds

What wild creature is more accessible to our eyes and ears, as close to us and everyone in the world, as universal as a bird?

— David Attenborough (Naturalist)

Apart from being amazing to watch, birds are a vital part of our ecosystem, in that they are brilliant at keeping garden pests away. You don't need much to encourage birds into your garden, or to your balcony, window or street. Experts don't recommend giving birds bread these days because it doesn't have much nutritional value for them and because it quickly goes off and mould is harmful to many birds. However there are plenty of other things you can put out for the birds, such as seeds, mealworms and fat balls. Making fat balls is fun, recycles kitchen scraps and birds absolutely love them! Remember not to leave them out in hot weather though as the fat can melt and stick to the birds' feathers.

Activity: Make fat balls for the birds

You will need:

- Vegetable suet
- Bird food mix (such as peanuts, birdseed, crumbs, grated cheese and currants
- Yogurt pots
- String
- Skewer or needle — ask an adult for help with this bit

As a guide, you should try to have about twice as much bird food mix compared to the amount of suet you use.

Instructions!

- Make a hole in the yogurt pot and thread a length of string through.
- Mix together your dry ingredients.
- Melt the suet in a big pan or microwaveable bowl — ask an adult to help.
- Stir the bird food mix and suet together.
- Spoon into the prepared yogurt pots and squash down firmly, making sure the string runs through the middle of the mixture.
- Leave to chill in the fridge.
- Cut away the yogurt pot and tie knots in the string to secure it.
- Hang from a tree, bush or pole.

You can keep spares in the freezer in a plastic bag, until you need them.

Visit the RSPB website to find pictures of birds to help you identify them.

So how did it go?
What birds did you spot?

How it works
Researchers from Exeter University have found that living close to bird life can help improve our wellbeing. Seeing birds in the garden distracts people from worries, gives them a moment of calm and helps to relax a stressed brain.

Create your own happy...
...by feeding the birds and keeping a note of what you spot. Remember just a few minutes a day spent watching the birds can boost your happiness, calm worries and release stress!

10. Give to Charity

Nobody ever became poor by giving
— Anne Frank (Diarist)

We're taught from when we are little that it's better to give than receive, but is there any truth in this? Yes! MRI scans show the part of our brain that gets excited about sweets and chocolate is also activated when we give to charity.

I remember one Christmas when my children and I collected and delivered lots of donations for a foodbank and rucksacks of goodies for a homeless charity. We all felt much happier that Christmas, but it wasn't just about the amount of the money or the stuff we had given, it was the time we had spent collecting things and working together with our friends who all wanted to join in too.

Here are some more happiness-boosting tips to help make your charity giving work best:

- Decide which causes you really care about.
- Give what you can afford — money and time are equally good!
- Find ways to use your specific skills and talents.
- Think about ways to work as a team with friends and family — FUNraising!

Activity: Charity project

Planning your own charity project and using your skills and time are going to bring the biggest happiness boost, to you and to those you help. It's important to choose a charity you are really passionate about helping.

Here are some ideas to get you started. You could:

- Collect pet food, blankets or towels for your local animal rescue shelter.
- Put together a rucksack for a homeless person — a thermos, soup with a ring pull, clean socks and pants, a jumper, hat, gloves, chocolate, a toothbrush, toothpaste.
- Donate to a local food bank for families in need — ask your grown-up if you can collect a couple of things each time you help with the shopping.
- Join a fun run or sponsored sport event — if you enjoy sport why not sign up for a race and ask friends and family to sponsor you?
- Hold a bake sale — when my daughter's school friend was poorly in hospital her class held a bake sale to raise money for toys and books for the children's ward.
- Wash Cars — could you offer to wash family and neighbours' cars for charity?

- Make something to sell — friendship bracelets, stress balls, hairbands. Can you think of small things your friends would love to buy?
- If raising money is tricky, don't forget you can volunteer your time.

So how did it go?

Did your project go according to plan? What did you give or raise? How did it make you feel? Who will benefit from this and how?

How it works

Thanks to MRI technology, which is used in brain scanners, researchers at the University of Oregon were able to see people's brain activity. When people donated to charity, the midbrain region of the brain lit up. This is the same part that gets excited about chocolate and yummy food! It seems our brains are wired to be happy about giving.

Create your own happy...

...by giving! We're happiest when we give to causes that we really care about, and when we have used our skills and time to help.

11. Learn about another culture

If you want to know what's important to a culture, learn their language. – Joanne Harris, (Author)

Cultural identity is the feeling of belonging to a particular group. It is part of how people see themselves and can be related to nationality, ethnicity, religion, social class, generation or locality.

This means our cultural identity is made up of lots of bits. Your parents or grandparents may be from different cultures, or the same. You might have moved house from one culture to another – north or south, city or country. You might have social, religious, sport or hobby groups too.

In Sweden, smorgasbord is a type of meal served buffet-style with lots of hot and cold dishes on the table. Just learning about one Swedish word teaches us that long, lazy buffets that bring family and friends together are important in Swedish culture. Specific foods are important, like herring and open sandwiches. Variety is important too.

Other languages have borrowed the word smorgasbord to mean 'a wide variety of things'.

Activity: Cook up a feast

Plan a meal for your family, the only rules being that the dish must come from another culture and should be something you haven't eaten or cooked for yourself before. If you fancy an extra challenge, maybe you want to prepare a smorgasbord of dishes from one country or from lots of different cultures? You could get the whole family involved.

How about a Danish open sandwich? Welsh cakes? Mexican burritos? Chinese noodles? Spanish omelette? French crepes? Mexican hot chocolate? Chinese fortune cookies? Italian pasta or pizza? An Indian curry?

So how did it go?
What did you make? What did your family think? What did it teach you about the country or culture?

How it works
Understanding other people's cultures can help us to be more kind and live together more happily. Different cultures can also help us think creatively and live more interesting lives too!

Create your own happy...

- Learning some words in another language
- Going to a festival or celebration
- Making something from another culture
- Talking to someone from a different culture
- Finding out a saying or a joke from another culture
- Visiting a shop from another culture
- Visiting a museum or ruins to find out about an ancient culture

12. Explore Your Values

*Values are like fingerprints. Nobody's are the same,
but you leave 'em all over everything you do*
— Elvis Presley, (Singer)

Elvis was right, our values are everywhere! We've talked a lot about values in this book, so now here comes some space for you to reflect on what your values are. You can use them to change your happiness and the world.

Activity: Create your coat of arms

The Romans and Greeks had symbols on their shields. By the 13th century, coats of arms were also used as emblems for families, inherited from one generation to the next.
It's time to create your own coat of arms!

Choosing your most important values can be tricky, but sometimes it's best to try and listen hard to your heart and choose the ones that seem to speak to you most.

Here are some of the values we have explored in the book, I bet you can think of more of your own too. Try and pick four or five values that seem most like YOU.

Using the word cloud and ideas of your own, decorate your coat of arms. Write your values on the shield. Can you think of colours, animals and other symbols to represent your values too?

And how about a motto? Here are some examples translated from other languages and from coats of arms.

Carpe diem – Seize the day!
Fortis in arduis – Brave in difficulties
Flead agus fuilte – Celebrate and welcome
Omnia pro bono – Always for the good
Liberté égalité fraternité –
Freedom, equality, togetherness

happy

So how did it go?

Were you surprised by the words that jumped out? Was it easy to choose your values?

How it works

Lots of very famous thinkers believe working out your core values helps you to live more happily and successfully. When our values and our actions don't match we can start to feel very uncomfortable or unhappy.

Create your own happy...

...by using your values to help you make choices. Your values can change over time, so keep thinking about them and writing them down.

13. Invent a Solution

An inventor fails 999 times, and if he succeeds once, he's in. He treats his failures simply as practice shots.
— Charles Kettering, (Inventor)

One of the most valuable lessons we can learn from inventors about changing the world is that failing is fine. In fact you HAVE TO FAIL lots of times in order to succeed!

Could you be like Easton LaChappelle who we mentioned in the introduction, and invent something that helps to change the world? Easton made his first robotic hand at the age of 14, using LEGO and fishing wire.

Activity: Be a problem solver

Ask a friend or family member for a problem they have had in the last week. You might need to ask a few people until you find a problem that gets your creative juices going.

Are your parents tired of the washing pile?
Does your dog keep barking at the postman?

Use the space below to sketch a solution. It could be a machine, an invention, a service, a company, an organisation or a job.

Allow your creativity to flow and feel free to be as silly as you like at first, you never know where this might take you. You could be inventing a solution for one problem but end up solving a totally different problem.

Did you know that so many inventions were ridiculed at first, from the lightbulb, to the umbrella, the taxi and vaccines. And ALL inventors failed before they came up with an invention that succeeded.

Be resilient, don't be knocked by failure, because as Einstein said, *'Anyone who has never made a mistake, has never tried anything new.'* Allow your creativity to flow.

So how did it go?

Did you get into the flow with your design? Did it spark more ideas? Did you enjoy inventing?

How it works

Some of the happiest people are dedicated to dealing with the most difficult problems such as finding solutions to homelessness or unsafe drinking water. Happiness can come from feeling we are making a difference.

Create your own happy...

...by keeping on looking for problems to solve and exercising your problem-solving skills. You never know what your ideas could start! And don't be afraid to fail.